Tom's Sunflower

Gingerbread
Single parents, equal families

Tom's Sunflower is dedicated to the hardworking
teams at Gingerbread, a charity that provides
expert advice, practical support and
campaigns for single parents.

Words by Hilary Robinson

www.hilaryrobinson.co.uk

Pictures by Mandy Stanley

www.mandystanley.com

STRAUSS HOUSE PRODUCTIONS

www.strausshouseproductions.com

www.thecoppertree.org

First published in Great Britain 2015

Text copyright © Hilary Robinson 2015

Illustrations copyright © Mandy Stanley 2015

Hilary Robinson and Mandy Stanley have asserted their rights

to be identified as the author and illustrator of this work under

the Copyright, Designs and Patents Act, 1988

British Library Cataloguing in Publication Data

A catalogue record for this book is available from the British Library

All rights reserved. ISBN-13: 978-0957124547

Printed in the UK

Tom's Sunflower

Hilary Robinson & Mandy Stanley

STRAUSS HOUSE
PRODUCTIONS

We're turning our classroom into a theatre because it's Skye and Amber's turn for 'Show and Tell'. Skye and Amber move about a lot with a travelling theatre so sometimes they come to our school and sometimes they go to other schools.

It's Mr Davis's turn soon. We're hoping he might tell us what his first name is.

Barnie

Hana

Alfie

Olivia

Erika

Amber →

Amber

Skye

Rupal

Skye →

Skye and Amber live in a caravan with bunk beds and their theatre is an
old circus tent. Amber told me once that she always had a wobbly tummy
when she felt a bit upset or when she had to start a new school again.

We all painted faces on wooden spoons for a puppet show but Hana didn't want to do it.

Mr Davis said that Hana was a bit sad at the moment. Hana talks to Mr Davis because he always says, 'a problem shared is a problem halved'.

Hana is sad because her mum and dad have split up and are going to live in different places.

At break, Alfie Tate and I played in the sandpit with Hana.

Mr Davis brought in sunflower seeds for us to plant.

Jake likes gardening. He says it's important that
each growing sunflower has 'its own space'.

Alfie thinks that if his sunflower grows up to the sky, there might be a giant at the top of it.

Hana cried at lunchtime.
She wanted her apple but didn't want her banana.

She used to like bananas but has changed her mind about them.
Mr Davis said that it was 'quite understandable'.

Alfie Tate ate her banana for her.

In the afternoon, Mr Davis did his 'Show and Tell'. He told us a story he had written called *Tom's Sunflower*. It was about a little boy whose parents were splitting up and he was upset about it. Sometimes Tom's tummy felt a bit wobbly.

Tom's parents were sad too.
Tom wanted everything to stay the same.

In time, Tom came to know that his mum and dad
found it easier living in different places.

He began to understand that even though his mum and dad didn't
live together anymore, they were still his mum and dad.

He also found that he made friends in different places.

Hana was quiet at first but then cheered up a bit when Amber held her hand.

Tom also came to understand that it wasn't
his fault that his parents split up.

Mr Davis said, 'Children often think it is their fault but it's definitely not the case.'

In the story, Tom's teacher suggested planting a sunflower seed.

He told Tom he would continue to grow
on sad days and happy days...

just like a sunflower would continue to grow
whether there were grey clouds or the sun was shining.

Mr Davis said that, like our sunflowers, we would always have our own little place in the world.

Mr Davis said he knew about these things
because guess who Tom grew up to be?

He grew up to be...Mr Davis!

Erika   Jake   Me   Amber   Alfie   Rupal   Holly

Hana

Mr Davis Tom ☺

Barnie   Skye

STRAUSS HOUSE
PRODUCTIONS

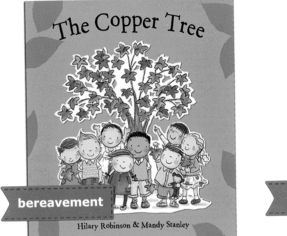

The Copper Tree

bereavement

Hilary Robinson & Mandy Stanley

Copper Tree Class

Christmas Surprise

the elderly

Hilary Robinson & Mandy Stanley

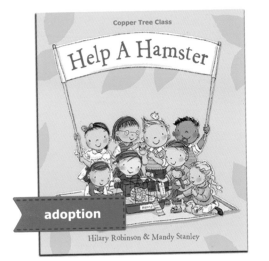

Copper Tree Class

Help A Hamster

adoption

Hilary Robinson & Mandy Stanley

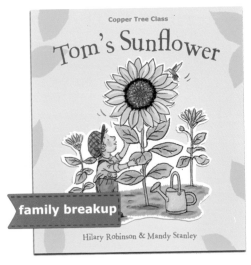

Copper Tree Class

Tom's Sunflower

family breakup

Hilary Robinson & Mandy Stanley

The Copper Tree Series

Helping Children to Help Themselves

www.strausshouseproductions.com

www.thecoppertree.org